VISUAL ILLUSIONS

Published and distributed by
TOBAR LIMITED
The Old Aerodrome, Worlingham, Beccles,
Suffolk, NR34 7SP, UK
www.tobar.co.uk

This edition printed in 2008

Printed in China

ISBN: 978 1 903230 16 9

INTRODUCTION

Visual Illusions is a fascinating collection of optical illusions, many of which have never before been published in this form. From classic illustrations of impossible figures to drawings of everyday objects which turn out to be extraordinary to scintillating graphic patterns which pulsate and change before your very eyes, the variety of different effects is almost endless!

Caltech cognitive vision scientist Al Seckel, the world's leading authority on illusions, has assembled this collection from the many thousands in his possession, especially for readers of this book.

MIRAGE

Where does the line of desert palm trees end, and the line of dromedaries begin?

This Saharan scene was created by digital artist Alice Klarke

Can you find the face of the woman that the man is serenading?
This figure/ground illusion is by Roger Shepard.

A MOUSE PLAYING HIDE AND SEEK WITH A CAT

Is the cat hiding from the mouse or the mouse hiding from the
cat? This reversible photo illusion was created by digital artist
Alice Klarke, based on an original drawing by artist Peter Brooks.

SAINT GEORGE AND THE DRAGON

Can you find both a portrait of Saint George and a depiction of his slaying of the dragon? Look at Saint George's hair to see the battle scene.

CORPORAL VIOLET

Can you find the three profiles (Napoleon, his wife and son) hidden between the leaves? This card, whose artist is unknown, originated around 1815.

VANITY

Can you see the skull? Charles Gilbert, an American magazine illustrator, created this classic illusion, entitled 'All is Vanity', some time around 1905. It was a very popular motif that was imitated many times, including by the Spanish surrealist Salvador Dali.

BECKONING BALUSTRADE

Can you find the figures hiding in between the columns? This figure/ground illusion is by Roger Shepard, and is a variation of the more famous 'faces/vase' illusion.

TODOROVIC'S GRADIENT CHESSBOARD ILLUSION

The gradients are real, but the small disks all have the same
luminance, even though some appear light, middle, and dark grey.

BRESSEN'S DOUBLE BRILLIANT ILLUSION
Does one diamond appear whiter than the other?

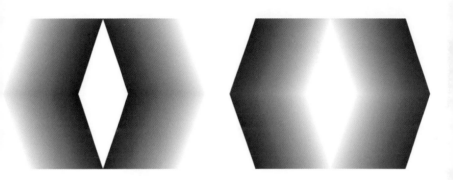

The two diamonds are identical in luminance.

THE COLOURED SCINTILLATING GRID ILLUSION

Move your eyes about this image, and the junctions will appear to scintillate and change their distribution.

PINNA'S SCINTILLATING LUSTRE ILLUSION

Do these circles appear to scintillate? This is a brand new illusion created by vision scientists Baingio Pinna and Lothar Spillman in 2002.

MELANCHOLY TUNES ON A FLEMISH WINTER'S DAY

How does the column come forward?

It can't! This is another impossible image, based on the original impossible triangle illusion by Roger Penrose.

BETWEEN ILLUSIONS AND REALITY

What is peculiar about the two openings?

If you cover up the top half of the illustration, the scene is perfectly possible. Look at it all together, however, and suddenly it is a lot more difficult to get into the entrances than you might think!

THE IMPOSSIBLE TERRACE

Are you seeing the balcony from the bottom or the top?
Both. This is an adaptation of Sandro del Piero's 'Folded Chess
Set', where perspective from both above and below is given
simultaneously.

KERSTEN'S BALL AND SHADOW ILLUSION

Are the balls in the two illustrations in different positions relative to the background?

No. The only difference between the two images is the placement of the cast shadows, making it appear as if the balls in the top illustration are resting on the surface and receding, while the balls in the bottom illustration appear to be rising above the surface.

L'Egistential Elephant

Will this elephant have difficulty walking?

At first glance this elephant seems to have all its legs, but look closely: none of them are attached to its body! Roger Shepard created this variation of the 'impossible fork' illusion.

What is wrong with the structure?

This is the first impossible print created by the Dutch graphic artist M.C Escher, in 1958. The top floor appears normal, but is in fact perpendicular to the bottom floor: impossible!

ESCHER'S WATERFALL

Can water really flow like this?

No! If you follow the flow of the water, you will see that it flows downwards and into the dirt until it again reaches the furthest and lowest point, which is identical with its nearest and highest point.

UNLIKELY WINDOW

This still life of a man sitting on a window ledge by Belgian artist Jos De Mey incorporates impossible triangles. The man holding the cube is in homage to the man holding the impossible cube in M.C Escher's 'Belvedere'.

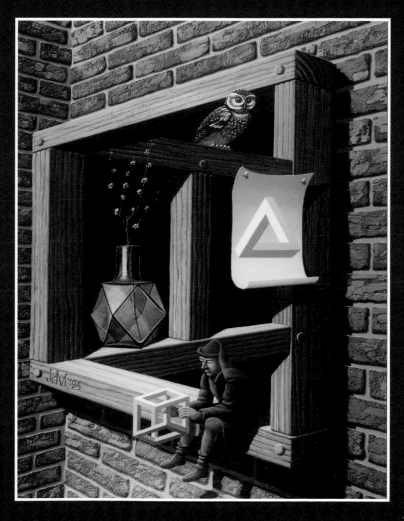

THE TWISTED CORD ILLUSION

Do the vertical lines appear to bend?

The lines are perfectly vertical and parallel to each other. The illusion is likely due to orientation-sensitive simple cells in the striate cortex, which interact to combine closely-spaced tilted lines into a single tilted line.

THE FRASER SPIRAL ILLUSION

Do you perceive a spiral or a series of concentric circles?
This is actually a series of concentric circles. The spiral is made
out of a series of overlapping arc segments within several
concentric circles of diminishing size. The Fraser spiral illusion
is so strong that it can even induce incorrect finger tracing!

WILCOX'S TWISTED CIRCLE ILLUSION

Although you may perceive a series of warped circles, this is actually a variation of the Fraser spiral, and also consists of concentric circles. James Wilcox, a twelve-year-old artist, created it.

PINNA'S INTERTWINING ILLUSION

Do these circles appear to intersect and cross over each other? They don't! If you tilt the book away from you, you will see that they are in fact concentric circles. This is a new type of directional illusion discovered recently by Italian vision scientist Baingio Pinna.

Kitaoka's Café Escher Illusion

These squares might appear to bulge in the centre, but if you check them with a straight edge, you will find they are all perfectly regular squares.

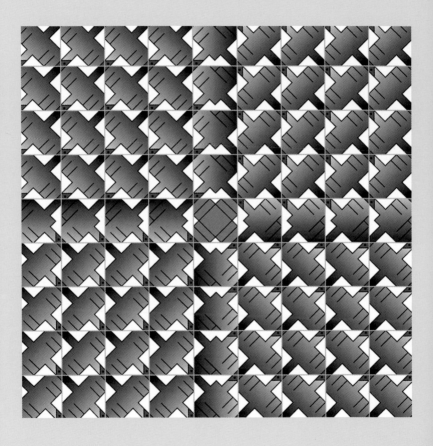

KITAOKA'S DISTORTED FIGURE

In this new twisted cord variation by Akiyoshi Kitaoka, the vertical or horizontal edges appear to be distorted and the figure appears to be wavy.

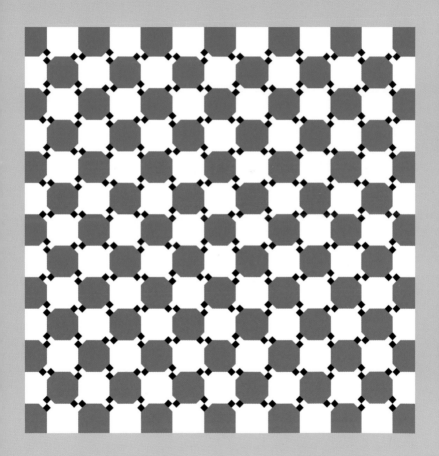

MEN WITH SUNGLASSES

Another twisted cord illusion by Akiyoshi Kitaoka which exhibits a relative motion. The vertical or horizontal edges appear to be distorted and each quarter region appears to move.

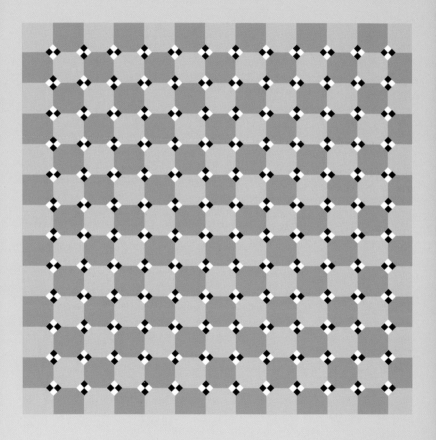

THE ZÖLLNER ILLUSION

The horizontal lines are parallel, but appear to tilt. This illusion was produced by Johann Zöllner in 1860, and it sparked off a huge interest in the whole subject of visual illusions.

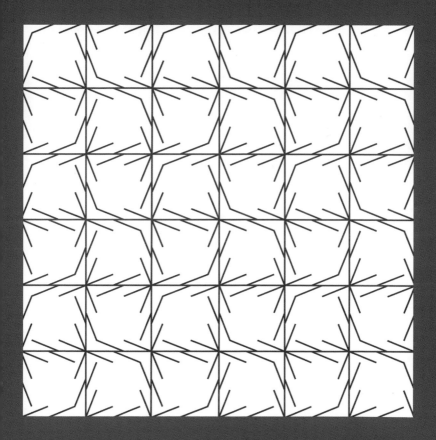

BLACKMORE'S TILT ORIENTATION ILLUSION

Do the vertical red lines in the two centre sections appear tilted with respect to their surrounds?

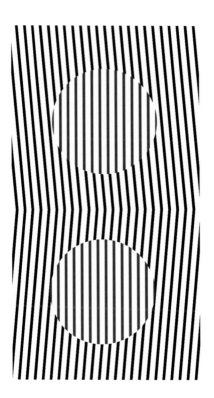

The lines are both vertical and parallel to each other. It is not known exactly what causes this illusion, but it is related to the Zöllner Illusion.

A Sudden Change of Direction

Stare at the fish in this illustration and they will face left and then suddenly change direction and face right, just like a real school of fish!

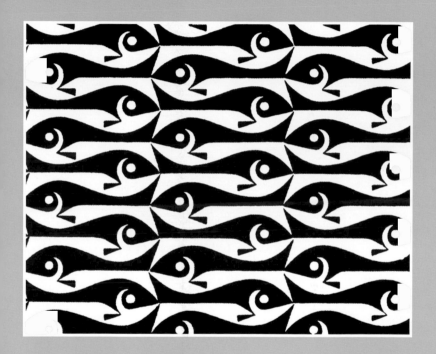

An Assimilation Illusion

Does the grey centre appear darker than its grey surround?

The grey value of both the centre square and its surround are identical.

THE CHEVREUL ILLUSION

In this illusion, each step from light to dark has a uniform brightness within the step. But at a border going from light to dark, the light edge makes the dark edge next to it appear darker. Put a pencil over the edge between any two stripes and the adjoining stripes will appear the same.

THE DIAMOND VARIATION OF THE CRAIK-O'BRIEN-CORNSWEET ILLUSION

Look at each row of diamonds. Does each row appear darker than the row above it?

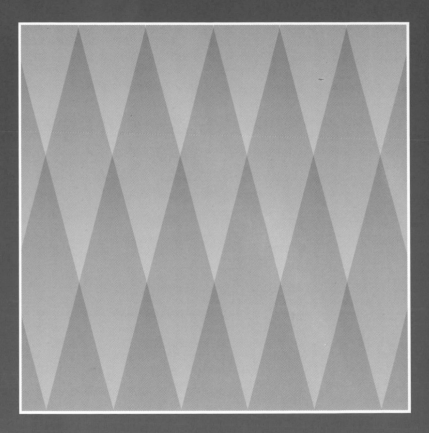

All the diamond shapes in this figure are in fact identical in luminance, but when combined in this pattern, the diamonds near the bottom are perceived as darker than those nearer the top.

PURVES AND LOTTO'S CONTRAST ILLUSION

Look at the striped figure. It appears to be made of two grey stripes that lie in between three white stripes. Yet, what you see is not what you get! The two grey stripes on the top of the figure are identical in luminance to the three white stripes on the front of the figure.

ADELSON'S CHECKERBOARD AND SHADOW ILLUSION

Examine the checkerboard pattern of both light and dark checks. Do the 'light' checks inside the shadow appear the same shade of grey as the 'dark' checks outside the shadow?

Todorovic's Dartboard Illusion

Do the 'light' and 'dark' regions, as indicated by the arrows, appear to be different? Believe it or not, they are identical.

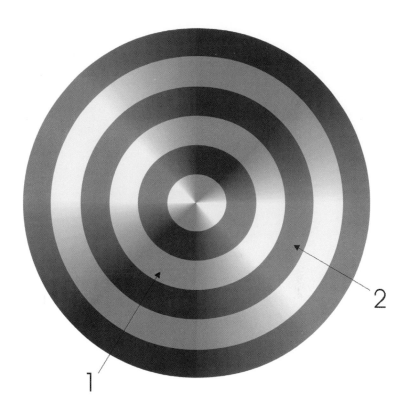

THE POGGENDORF ILLUSION

Which coloured line intersects with the white line?

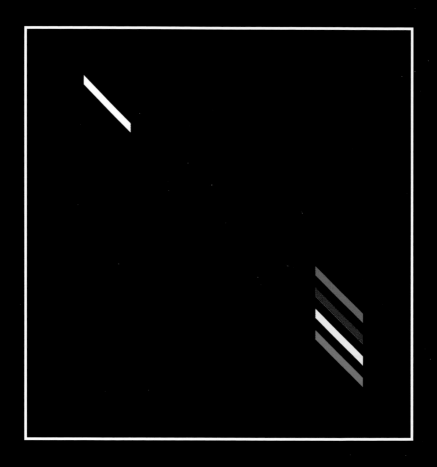

The white line intersects with the yellow line, even though you may not perceive it that way. This illusion is one of the most famous, and although it is over 140 years old, there is as yet no theory to fully account for it.

THE TOP HAT ILLUSION

Does the height of the hat appear greater than its width?

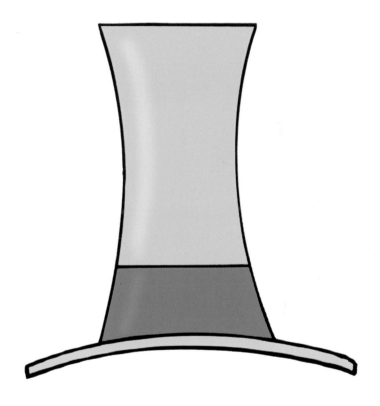

The height of the hat and its width are the same. This is a variation of the classic inverted T illusion, which has been attributed to Johann Oppel. The illusion also persists if the figure is rotated 90°.

DAY'S SINE WAVE ILLUSION

Do some of the vertical line segments appear to be unequal in length?

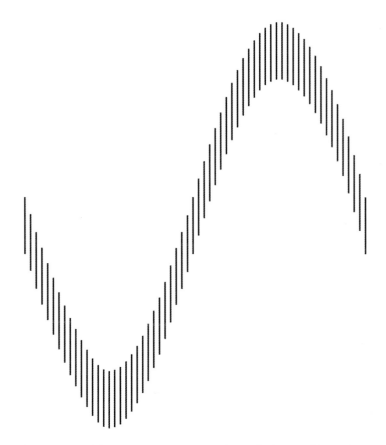

All the vertical line segments are in fact of identical length!

THE EBBINGHAUS ILLUSION

Which inner circle appears larger in size?

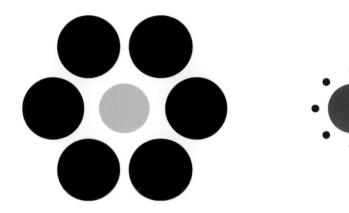

The inner circles are identical in size, even though the circle with the smaller ones surrounding it appears bigger than the circle surrounded by larger ones. However, this effect decreases as the distance between the larger and smaller circles increases.

NEON COLOUR SPREADING

Do you perceive a faint bluish colour within the square region on the left?

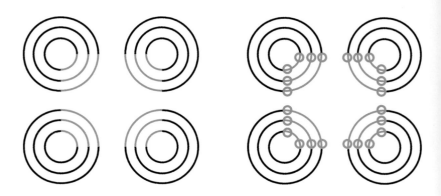

The square region is in fact completely white. On the right, when circles are placed at the edges of the illusory square, the neon colour spreading disappears.

PURVES AND LOTTO'S RUBIK'S CUBE COLOUR ILLUSION

How much darker does the brown square on the top of the Rubik's cube appear to be than the yellow square that is in the middle of the side within the shadow?

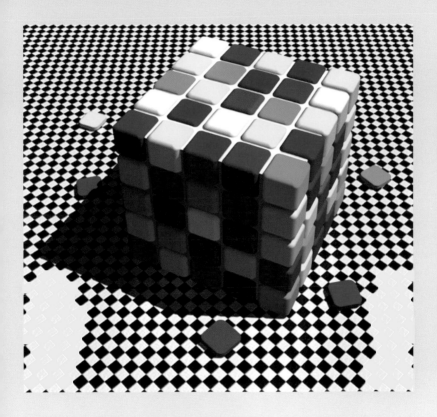

Unbelievably, the 'brown' square is identical to the 'yellow' square! To test this, cover up the rest of the Rubik's Cube and check both squares.

CHROMATIC COLOUR ASSIMILATION

Red appears to be magenta or orange.
This is because the red colour is influenced by the colour of the
background on which it is placed, and by the lines which are
overlaid.

KITAOKA'S RED SPIRAL

Red again appears to be orange or magenta. This is another
illusion created by Japanese vision scientist Akiyoshi Kitaoka.

Balls at Many Different Levels

The depth of the mesh tends to be flush with the depth of the circle at which observers fixate in this illusion from Japanese vision scientist Akiyoshi Kitaoka.

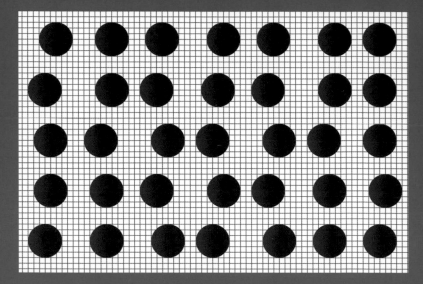

A WALLPAPER ILLUSION

Focus on the two dots at the top of this illusion, and bring the book closer to your face until the two dots become three. The image will appear in depth.

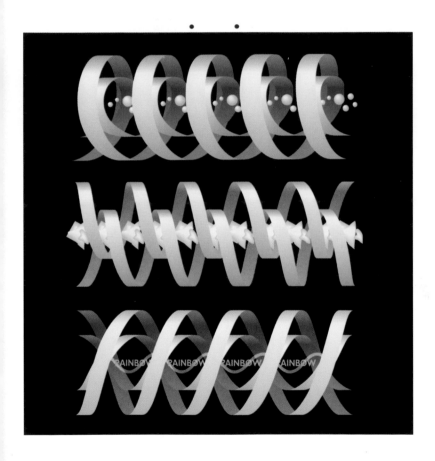

LEVIANT'S ENIGMA

Stare at the very centre of this image. Do you see motion in the blue rings? In what direction are they travelling? Do they change direction? How does the direction of motion in one ring relate to the direction of motion in another ring?

WAVES

Move your eyes across this image and you should see a powerful illusory depth motion. You may also see a stereo illusion and the waves may oscillate.

THE OUCHI ILLUSION

If you move your eyes across the image or slowly shake the image, the centre section will appear to separate in depth and move slightly in a direction opposite to its surround.

OUT OF FOCUS

If you move your eyes across this image or slowly shake the image, the inset will appear to fluctuate in this variation of the Ouchi Illusion.

PINNA'S SEPARATING SQUARES ILLUSION

If you move your eyes across this image or slowly shake the image, the randomly placed centre squares will appear to separate in depth and move slightly differently to their surrounding squares.

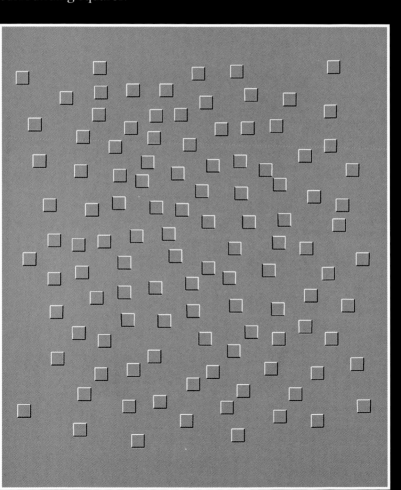

THE PINNA-BRELSTAFF REVOLVING CIRCLES ILLUSION

Stare at the centre of the image, slowly move your head towards the page, and then away from it. The circles should counter-rotate. When you move your head away from the page, both motions reverse direction, reversing the direction of the illusion.

Pinna's Separating Lines Illusion

If you move this figure up and down, the illusory motion is left and right. If you move the sheet left and right, the illusory motion is up and down.

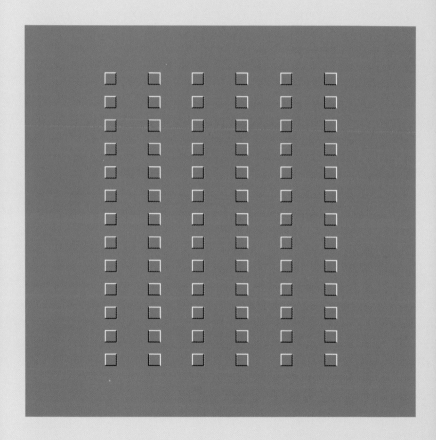

KITAOKA'S SPINNING VORTEX ILLUSION

Move your head towards and away from this image, and it should slightly rotate. Scientists do not yet know exactly why this happens, although the dots must have sharp edges for this illusion to work.

KITAOKA'S SPINNING WHEEL ILLUSION

You do not have to move either your head or the image to make this illusion work. Just stare at the image and each circle will appear to rotate. In addition, the concentric circles appear to be spirals. This illusion works best when seen through peripheral vision.

FERRY BOAT

You do not have to move your head or the image to make this illusion work. Just stare at the image and the slanted grey bars will appear to move in a horizontal direction. This illusion works best when seen through peripheral vision.

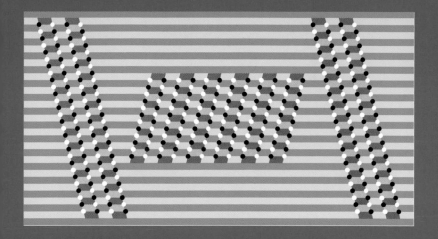

KITAOKA'S MOVING LINES

You do not have to move your head or the image to make this illusion work. Just stare at the image and the horizontal lines will appear to move. This illusion works best when seen through peripheral vision.

Kitaoka's Heat Devil

Stare at this image and it will appear to pulsate and fluctuate, very much like the movement of air that you see above a heated surface, known as a heat devil.

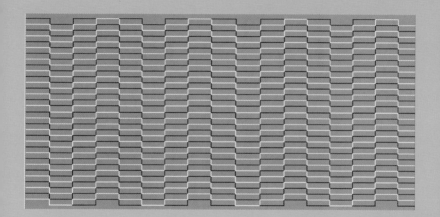

SHEPARD'S TABLETOP ILLUSION

Are these two table tops different in size and shape? Look carefully before you answer!

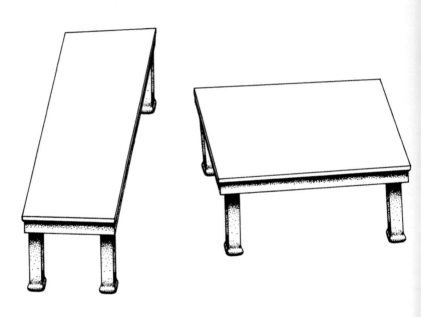

The two table tops are exactly identical in size and shape. You can test this by tracing them out and comparing them.

An Illusion of Extent

Which line is longer, AB or CD?

Although they appear to be dramatically different in length, line
AB and CD are equal.

Terra Subterranea

Is the background figure larger than the foreground figure? It would appear to be that way, yet they are both identical in size. Again, you can test this by tracing the outline of one and laying it on top of the other.

THE HALLWAY ILLUSION

This scene looks perfectly natural, except for the man in the lower right-hand corner, who appears to be a midget. Yet he is identical in size to the figure in the background.

THE MÜLLER-LYER ILLUSION IN PERSPECTIVE

Which red line is longer?

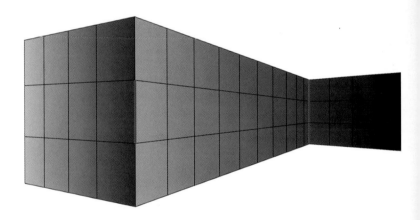

They are both identical in length. Although the Müller-Lyer illusion is not a perspective illusion, it can be augmented through perspective cues, as in this example.

A Foreshortening Illusion

Visually estimate, but do not mathematically calculate, the circumference of the cylinder's rim. Would you say that your estimate is less than, equal to, or more than the height of the cylinder?

The height of the cylinder is in fact equal to its circumference.

ONE HEAD OR TWO?

Do you perceive one head or two profiles?

This is a very nice example of an ambiguous illustration that 'flip-flops' in meaning, giving either a single face partially obscured by the candlestick, or two faces in profile on either side of the candlestick. This is a variation on the vase illusion.

AN OLD OR A YOUNG WOMAN?

Can you find the profile of an old woman and a young woman?
This well-known illusion dates back to the nineteenth century,
when it first began to appear on puzzle trading cards.

THE FLOWERING OF LOVE

Can you find the lovers in the flowers?

Look carefully at the petals of the rose; they form the outline of a kissing couple, or that of a single rose. Swiss artist Sandro Del Prete created this beautiful ambiguous illusion.

MARLENE

Can you find the portrait of Marlene Dietrich?
Mexican artist Octovio Ocampo created this charming scene of
the famous 1940s film star.

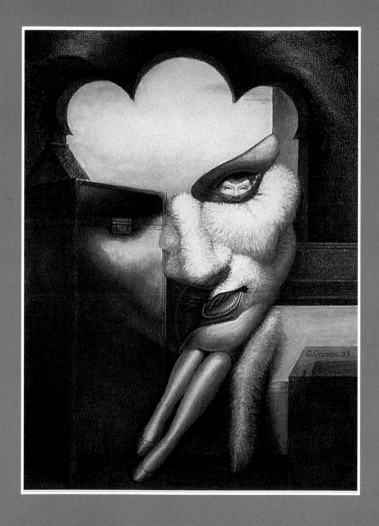

ANGELS

Can you find both the heads and bodies of angels?
The head and hand of the large angel contain the bodies of four
smaller angels.

THE MYSTERIOUS LIPS

Do you perceive the face?

The Spanish surrealist Salvador Dali, who was fascinated by ambiguous imagery, entitles this scene 'The Mysterious Lips that Appeared on the Back of my Nurse', painted in 1941.

VISION OF DON QUIXOTE

How many hidden faces can you find?
There are several hidden faces in this illustration of the classic
Cervantes character, but the main scene is ambiguous with a
portrait of Don Quixote and his faithful servant Sancho Panza.

JASTROW'S DUCK/RABBIT ILLUSIONS

This is one of the most famous and classic of all illusions, which was created by the American psychologist Joseph Jastrow in 1888. Depending upon how you view the image, you can perceive either a rabbit or a duck.

A HIDDEN PORTRAIT IN A STILL LIFE OF VEGETABLES

Do you perceive a face or a collection of fruit?
This is Giuseppe Arcimboldo's classic portrait of the Emperor
Rudolph II.

A SIMULTANEOUS CONTRAST ILLUSION
Is the horizontal bar the same value of grey throughout?

Yes, it is. You can check this by covering everything but the bar.